marie claire

hair

acknowledgements

I would like to thank Catie Ziller, Anne Wilson, Matt Handbury and Jackie Frank for their ongoing support and the opportunity to develop this series. Thank you to everyone at Murdoch Books and Merehurst Publishing who has been involved in this project for their continuous hard work. I would also like to say a big thank you to photographer Chris Craymer for his inspiration, endless enthusiasm and creativity, and for capturing the spirit of this book on film. Thank you, too, to Martyn Gayle and Attracta Courtney for their hard work and fab hair and make-up. Special thanks to Susie for all her hard work and great organising for the shoot production.

Most of all I would like to thank those closest to me who supported me from start to finish, especially Danny, my sister Susie, Stewart and Lottie for being there when things got tough, my mum Brenda for her inspiration, my dad Brian for his constant drive, and my grandma for her worldly advice. Thanks also to Nicola, Sam and Michael, who kept me smiling. I couldn't have got this far without you all.

Special thanks to Lavish Locations, Melanie at Aurelia, Penhaligons, Melissa Hargreeves Millinery for hat block hire (p. 49), tel 44 1488 72890; Trendco for the loan of the hair pieces and wigs, tel 44 20 7221 2646. Thank you for the loan of the following items for photography: Cath Kidson dress (p. 15), tel 44 20 7221 4000; Muji underwear (pp. 61, 68), tel 44 20 7221 9360; Liza Bruce swimwear (p. 62), tel 44 20 7235 8423; Erickson Beamon tiara (p. 66), tel 44 20 7259 0202; Helen David for English Eccentrics dress (p. 71).

marie claire

hair

jane campsie
photography by chris craymer

MURDOCH BOOKS®
Sydney • London • Vancouver • New York

contents

healthy

resilient

lustrous

our hair

silky

shiny

soft

healthy hair

Hair is a gauge of our inner health. When in good health our hair is lustrous, resilient and soft. Illness, stress, fatigue and medications can leave our hair dull, lifeless and hard to handle. Maintaining our health paves the way to beautiful hair. Hair is made up of keratin protein cells. Each strand consists of three layers: the cuticle, cortex and medulla. The protective outer layer is made up of tiny scales known as cuticles. When hair is in optimum condition, these scales lie flat and the hair looks shiny and feels soft. Damaged hair is dull and brittle as a result of the cuticles having been physically or chemically damaged. Beneath the cuticles lie the fibre-like cells that make up the cortex. These give hair its strength and elasticity.

Melanin, the pigment that determines our natural hair colour, is also found in the cortex. The inner layer of the hair, the medulla, is made up of soft keratin cells and is believed to supply the cortex and cuticles with nutrients and other vital substances to sustain condition, health and resilience.
Each hair goes through three growth phases: the anagen phase, which lasts up to 4 years, when hair actively grows; the catagen phase, which lasts up to 20 days, when hair stops growing but cellular activity continues; and the telogen phase, which lasts up to 90 days, when hair stops growing completely. Usually, 93% of our hair is in the anagen phase, 1% in the catagen phase and 6% in the telogen phase.

hair aggressors

uv radiation

The sun's ultraviolet rays play havoc with the hair, robbing it of essential moisture, causing colour to fade and burning the scalp. Even on a cloudy day, 90% of the sun's rays penetrate the clouds, so it's advisable to shield the hair from damaging sunlight at all times. Look for styling preparations that contain the UV filter Parsol MCX. Better still, wear a hat or scarf. This will also guard against heatstroke. To protect the scalp from the damaging rays of the sun, massage sunscreen into the skin and, if redness occurs, liberally apply aloe vera gel.

weather extremes

Wind and harsh weather conditions have a drying effect on the hair. Strong winds can make the hair brittle and dry, and in freezing temperatures hair picks up static electricity, becoming flyaway. In the snow, UV rays are intensified by the reflected light, so ensure your hair gets extra protection.

pollution alert

Smoke, pollution and city grime can build up on the hair, making it look dull and lifeless. The by-products of cigarette smoke and natural gas from cookers can also discolour the hair. To banish the effects of pollutants, wash your hair regularly and keep brushes and combs clean. If hair smells of smoke or cooking and you don't have time to wash it, brush thoroughly and then spray a fine mist of perfume onto your brush or comb and run through the hair. Don't spray perfume directly into the hair—the alcohol in it can have a drying effect.

central heating

Central heating draws moisture from the hair and scalp and can cause static. To reduce the drying effects of central heating, place large bowls of water near radiators, or use humidifiers. To tame static, flyaway hair, spray a fine mist of hairspray onto a hairbrush and run through the hair.

hair aggressors

stressful situations

Stress has a negative impact on the hair. It can, at the least, cause a dry and flaky scalp, and at worst it can accelerate hair loss. Alopecia areata is the appearance of temporary bald patches. In roughly half the cases of people suffering from this condition, stress is the cause. If you lead a stressful lifestyle, step up your intake of B vitamins, which are essential for healthy hair. Yoga is beneficial, too. Not only will it calm the mind; certain positions, such as headstands and shoulder-stands, are a great way of getting blood to the scalp.

heat styling

Limit your use of heat-styling appliances, as these can leave your hair dry and brittle. Allow your hair to dry naturally whenever possible, and always use a protective styling product to help retain the hair's moisture and to impart shine.

water irritation

Hard water, salts, chemicals and chlorine interfere with hair condition, leaving a build-up on the hair shaft and in some instances causing discolouration. After exposing hair to chlorinated water, wash immediately. If hair is coloured, use a protective preparation before swimming, or slick wax through the hair. If you live in a soft-water area, apply shampoo and conditioner sparingly, as they can be difficult to rinse out.

harsh haircare

Find haircare products that work in harmony with your hair type. Harsh preparations will strip the hair of its natural oils, leading to dry and dull-looking hair. Products that leave a residue on the hair will make it limp and lank. If you are uncertain as to your exact hair type, ask your hairdresser to analyse it and to recommend a suitable haircare regimen.

healthy options

nutritional benefits

What we eat plays a significant role in determining the health of our hair and scalp. A diet rich in protein is vital for healthy hair. Good sources include lean meat, poultry, fish, cheese, eggs, nuts, seeds and pulses. If you want to improve the strength and natural shine of the hair, step up your intake of fish, seaweed, almonds, brazil nuts, yoghurt and cottage cheese. Cut down on caffeine and alcohol. These stimulants hamper the absorption of minerals essential for hair health.

get physical

Hair needs oxygen to remain healthy. Regular exercise encourages good blood flow, which in turn ensures that vital oxygen and nutrients are carried to the roots of the hair via the blood. Research has shown that 30 minutes of cumulative exercise daily is sufficient to keep us healthy.

supplementary benefits

Many common hair complaints, such as dandruff and flaky scalps, can be linked to vitamin or mineral deficiencies. The following supplements can help to improve hair and scalp condition: beta-carotene (which works as an anti-oxidant), vitamin B complex, vitamin C, omega-3, starflower oil, selenium and zinc. Consult an expert for advice before taking supplements.

breathe deeply

Breathing properly is essential for expelling wastes and oxygenating the body. The scalp requires oxygen to maintain healthy hair and hair growth. Most of us rely on shallow breaths. Try this daily exercise to improve maximum breathing potential: inhale deeply through the nose, counting to four, then exhale through the nose, counting to six. Repeat the exercise several times.

discerning matters

hormonal matters

The hair is affected by hormonal changes, especially during puberty and pregnancy. The sudden surge of hormones in the first three months of pregnancy can increase the activity of the sebaceous glands, making the hair much oilier. Overcome this by washing frequently with a mild shampoo. For the remainder of a pregnancy, hair usually looks its best. Each hair has a prolonged growth period, so it looks thick and lustrous. After giving birth, when hormones are readjusting, hair may not look or feel its best. It is also normal to experience seemingly excessive hair loss around 12 weeks after the birth. This is just the shedding of hair that would normally have been lost in the 9 months previous. When pregnant, try taking wheatgerm, a natural source of vitamin B important for healthy hair. It is not advisable to subject the hair to chemical processing during pregnancy. If you want to colour your hair, opt for vegetable colours.

hair loss

On average we lose between 20–30 hairs every day. This is perfectly natural. However, temporary hair loss can occur during pregnancy, or from stress, illness or taking medication. It usually regrows. Traction hair loss occurs when the hair is forced too tightly during braiding. It disrupts the hair follicles, causing scar tissue to form and leading to hair loss. Hereditary hair loss affects 10% of women. There are many treatments on offer, but many promise more than they deliver. As we age, the cells that form and support the hair follicle stop dividing and eventually die, prohibiting new hair growth. To help prevent this, avoid highly alkaline shampoos and silicone-based products, rinse hair thoroughly, and massage the scalp regularly to prevent asphyxiation of the hair follicles. Increase your intake of biotin, a vitamin B complex which is found in cauliflower, nuts and eggs.

hair science

THE NUMBER of hair strands on a person's head is genetically determined. Between 80 000 and 120 000 hairs is typical, but blondes have more and redheads have fewer. Women generally have more hair than men do.

OUR HAIR grows 12 mm (1/2 inch) per month. The growth rate steps up during the summer months and while we sleep. If hair is never cut, it grows to about 107 cm (42 inches) in length before falling out. A single strand of hair lives for up to 7 years.

WE LOSE between 20 and 30 hairs each day. These hairs are usually replaced with new hairs, so the loss goes undetected.

AGEING MAKES the hair drier and more brittle. Colour changes also occur as melanin production slows down and eventually ceases. As a result, hair appears colourless, or what is known to us as 'grey'.

HEALTHY HAIR should be able to stretch up to 30% of its normal length before breaking. It should also be able to absorb its weight in water. Human hair is stronger than copper wire of the same thickness.

SEBUM IS the hair's natural lubricant and protector. Stress, illness, hormonal changes, harsh haircare products and certain medications can interfere with the activity of the sebaceous glands, increasing sebum production to make the hair greasy.

HAIR COLOUR is determined by the pigment melanin. The shape and number of melanin granules in the hair shaft will dictate our natural hair colour. People with a large number of elongated melanin granules have black hair, those with slightly fewer elongated granules have brown hair, and people with even fewer and smaller granules have blonde hair. Those with oval or spherical granules have red hair.

normal

curly

fine

hair types

flyaway

thirsty

oily

hair types

Our hair type and texture is genetically determined, but external influences play a vital role in determining the look and feel of hair. At different stages in our lives, when hormone levels change, and depending on whether we are taking medication, suffering from stress, lacking nutrients in our diet or feeling under the weather, our hair condition will vary. Hair is a good indicator of the state of our general health.

One of the most common problems that hairdressers see is the wrong product being used for a particular hair type. If you are uncertain as to whether your hair is fine, medium or coarse, pluck one strand from your head and try to break it.

If it snaps easily, it's fine in texture; if it requires more effort to break, the chances are your hair is medium in texture; and if it is near impossible to break, your hair is coarse. Gauge your hair type and then choose products accordingly.

Remember to adapt your haircare regime from season to season, taking into account the moisture content of the hair. For example, in the winter, when wind, central heating and cool temperatures can leave hair feeling dry, use moisturising shampoos and conditioners. During the summer, if you are exposed to very humid conditions, switch to a mild shampoo and a leave-in conditioner to help combat any possible frizz.

hair types

thirsty hair

Hair becomes dry, dehydrated and brittle as a result of a lack of sebum. Dry hair usually only stretches half as far as a normal strand of hair. The condition is often caused by excessive heat styling, chemical processing, environmental aggressors, UV radiation, seawater, chlorine, mismanagement, neglect and harsh haircare products. To help regulate sebum production, massage the scalp with almond or jojoba oil. Leave the oil on the hair for 10 minutes before shampooing. Do this with a moisturising shampoo and give the scalp a good, invigorating massage while lathering up. This will step up circulation and help distribute sebum more effectively. Follow up with conditioner, and once in a while treat your hair to intensive masks and hair packs to redress the moisture balance. Brush your hair regularly to stimulate the scalp and to distribute existing oil through the hair.

curly hair

Curly hair can look fantastic, provided it is looked after properly. It naturally has a tendency to look dull and lifeless, as the cuticles do not lie flat, and it can be dry and hard to handle, often ending up as a frizzy mess. To maintain curly hair, use a moisturising shampoo and conditioner. Alternate with a different shampoo every sixth wash, as hair becomes accustomed to certain ingredients. Leave curly hair to dry naturally, whenever possible, or if you must use a dryer, use a diffuser attachment on it. Never brush or comb curly hair—this only promotes frizz. Use your fingers to break up the texture instead. Another way to help overcome frizz is to look for styling preparations that repel moisture: serums and pomades are a good choice. Alternatively, try using a leave-in conditioner after shampooing. It won't overload the hair but it will help retain moisture and prevent frizz.

hair types

fine hair

Fine hair can be hard to handle and needs to be properly looked after. Wash frequently with a mild shampoo to prevent the hair becoming greasy, limp and lank. If regular conditioners have a tendency to weigh hair down, try a leave-in formula instead. Having your hair coloured can make the hair appear thicker, as the chemical processing makes the hair shaft swell. Also, the choice of colour can create the illusion of added volume. To make dark hair look thicker, add gold and rich copper highlights; to enhance blonde hair, weave in deep-brown streaks. The highlights need to be chunky to achieve the right effect. When styling, look for preparations that contain heat-activated ingredients that will help boost the volume and texture. Steer clear of products containing silicones or waxes, as these will weigh the hair down. Avoid one-length hairstyles and go for a layered or graduated style instead, to create the illusion of added body.

afro hair

Afro hair is usually coarse and dry, making it susceptible to damage and breakage. To look after the hair, use intensive pre-shampoo treatments to help hydrate the scalp and hair, massage the scalp regularly to encourage oil production, shampoo as often as necessary, and only lather once. Give the hair a hot-oil treatment once a month. If you feel the need to tame very curly Afro hair, have your hair demi-permed. Demi-perming is a process which transforms tight curls into larger, looser ones by weaving the hair onto rollers to redefine the shape. To maintain, use special curl activators and moisturising sprays. Straightening or relaxing—a chemical process that has the reverse action of perming—is another option for Afro hair. Chemical relaxers come in different strengths to suit different hair textures and styles. Use a natural bristle brush for hair that has been relaxed, and a wide-toothed Afro comb for curly styles.

hair types

oily hair

When the scalp's oil-producing glands produce too much sebum, the hair becomes greasy and lank. To ensure sebum levels do not build up, wash the hair frequently with a mild shampoo; harsh formulations will only strip the hair and exacerbate the activity of the sebaceous glands, accelerating oil production. Once a week, rub jojoba oil (which is similar to the hair's natural oil) into the scalp and leave on overnight. Adding oil like this tricks the hair into believing it is producing the oil itself and helps regulate sebum production. Help combat greasiness by limiting exposure to hot water and excessive heat styling. Colorants can also help, as they alter the porosity of the hair. If you suffer from oily hair, nutritionists advise steering clear of fried and processed foods and eating more fresh fruits and vegetables.

coloured hair

Colouring your hair can improve its overall texture and appearance, but subjecting the hair to chemical processing will change the hair's pH balance, often making it dry, brittle and prone to damage and breakages. Opt for conditioning colorants and always use a shampoo and conditioner formulated for coloured hair. These products provide reparative action and will help the colour to remain true. Steer clear of anti-dandruff shampoos, as they can accelerate colour fade. Treat the hair to an intensive rehydrating treatment once a week, or whenever you feel it is needed, if your hair is dry and brittle. Always protect coloured hair from ultraviolet light, as the invisible rays will accelerate the speed at which the colour fades. Also, limit the use of heat-styling appliances if you wish to preserve hair condition and colour.

making headway

BRUSH YOUR hair before shampooing. This will remove dirt, loosen dead skin cells from the scalp and make the hair tangle-free, in addition to improving circulation to the scalp for healthier hair.

FORGET THE myth that you should brush your hair 100 times a day. Over-zealous brushing can in fact tear the hair and remove too many of the hair's natural oils, leaving it dry and dull.

A COMB with rounded teeth will not damage your hair or harm the scalp. To test the smoothness of a comb, rub the teeth against the palm of your hand.

WASH HAIRBRUSHES and combs regularly with hot soapy water and leave to dry naturally. Throw out brushes and combs with broken bristles or teeth, as these can damage the scalp and hair.

STEER CLEAR of combined shampoos and conditioners unless you have healthy, resilient hair. They will not be sufficient to treat hair types needing additional care.

NEVER RINSE your hair in bath water: dirty water is not conducive to clean hair, and the water will probably contain alkaline soap residues which will cling to the hair, making it look dull.

EVERY TIME you shampoo your hair you lose about 20 hairs. Don't be alarmed by this hair loss; according to the experts, it's perfectly normal.

FREQUENT HAIRCUTS or trims—say, one every 6 to 8 weeks—will help to maintain the condition and strength of the hair, in addition to retaining the overall shape of the hairstyle and banishing split ends.

cleanse

condition

treat

haircare

revitalise

rehydrate

replenish

cleansing regime

washing it

Hair should be washed only as needed. Over-washing and the use of harsh shampoos can strip the hair of its natural oils. If, on the other hand, hair is left unwashed for too long, it can become a breeding ground for bacteria. Look for a shampoo suited to your hair type or use a mild formulation. For the best results, shampoo once only. Unless the hair is really dirty, two washes are not necessary. If you have used oil-based or greasy preparations to style hair, apply shampoo to dry hair, wash out and then wash as normal. Shampoos are detergent based and work by swelling the hair shaft and lifting the cuticle. They also carry an electric charge which causes individual hair strands to react with one another, producing static. After shampooing, hair is left with a negative charge. Conditioners contain positively charged agents that bond with the negative charge of the hair.

coming clean

Water that is too hot will agitate the scalp and increase the activity of the oil-producing glands, but cool water will not remove grease and other stubborn impurities. Wash your hair in warm water, and always under the shower head—washing in bath water is not conducive to thorough cleansing.
It is a good idea to alternate shampoo formulations—every six to eight washes is ideal—since hair becomes accustomed to a particular shampoo, leaving a residue on the hair.
Alternatively, use a deep-cleansing formula once a week or once a fortnight, depending on the condition of your hair. Hair that has been coloured or chemically treated has an altered pH balance and needs special treatment. Don't use ordinary shampoos, as these will strip the colour from the hair; choose instead a shampoo specially formulated for colour-treated hair to gently cleanse the hair and maintain the colour.

extra care

conditioning care

Always use a conditioner. Hair is left with a negative charge after shampooing, and the cuticles are dishevelled, making the hair susceptible to damage. Conditioners contain positively charged agents that bond with the negative charge of cleansed hair. They ensure that the cuticles lie flat so the hair appears healthy and shiny. For best results, do not apply conditioner to the scalp; run it through the lengths and ends of the hair only, then rinse out. Most conditioners only coat the hair shaft, so leaving a conditioner on for longer than the specified time will be of no added benefit. When rinsing the hair, always aim the flow of water down the hair shaft, not against the shaft. If you have fine hair or find that most conditioners leave your hair too soft and hard to manage, try using a leave-in conditioner. This won't weigh the hair down, but it will boost hydration and shine and reduce static.

treatment masks

When hair is dull, lifeless and hard to handle, treat it with a revitalising hair mask. The conditioning and reparative properties of a mask are superior to those of a basic conditioner. Moisturising treatments will counteract the dryness of hair, making it soft to the touch and more resilient. If hair is damaged from environmental hazards or chemical processing, look for a protein mask that will help repair hair and restore strength and elasticity. Apply treatment masks to freshly shampooed hair and leave on for the specified time. To increase the conditioning properties, apply the mask and then wrap the hair in a hot towel, or use a hair-dryer to heat the applied preparation. Try to avoid using hot-oil treatments. Although they are beneficial for rehydrating dry, damaged locks, they can be difficult to wash out of the hair. Excessive washing to remove the oil will undo the benefits of the treatment.

scalp treats

head massage

Treating yourself to a regular head massage not only nourishes the hair and scalp, it helps relieve tension and stimulate circulation. Either massage your head while shampooing, or do it as a pre- or post-washing treatment using massage oils. Gently run your fingers through your hair, starting from the forehead and working over the crown and down to the nape of the neck. Repeat several times to relax yourself. Then, using the pads of the fingertips and working in small, circular motions, massage from the forehead to the back of the neck. This will stimulate and soothe the scalp. Then take large sections of the hair and gently lift them upwards, away from the scalp. Work over the head, gently pulling sections of hair in this way. Finish by working over the scalp once again, from the forehead to the nape of the neck, using vigorous, short strokes.

massage oils

You can massage the scalp with or without oil. If using an oil blend, massage in an hour before washing or leave on overnight (use a towel to protect your pillowcase) and rinse out in the morning. To concoct a blend, mix 30 ml (1 fl oz) of a base oil such as jojoba or almond oil with three drops of essential oil. Never apply essential oils directly to the scalp. If you are suffering from a dry, itchy scalp, treat using rose or chamomile essential oil blended with a base oil. To help regulate dandruff, concoct a blend using essences of geranium, cedar-wood and chamomile oil. To treat an oily scalp, use cedarwood, chamomile, eucalyptus or lavender oil. To treat hair loss, use lavender, patchouli or rosemary essential oil. Always consult a qualified aromatherapist before using essential oils, especially if you are pregnant.

scalp problems

dandruff control

Dandruff should not be confused with dry skin. Dryness is often a hereditary condition, or is caused by a change in climate, harsh sun exposure and heat styling. Dandruff, on the other hand, is a fungal infection typified by loose, oily flakes of skin. It is often caused by stress, poor circulation, insufficient nutrients, the use of harsh haircare preparations and not rinsing effectively after shampooing. Dandruff cannot be cured, but it can be controlled. To help regulate the condition, wash your hair every day or every other day with a mild shampoo. Avoid tar-based formulations and preparations containing metal oxides, as these can be too harsh. Select a product that has a natural base, and always rinse it out well. Do not pick or touch the scalp after treatment. Acupuncture, Chinese medicine and herbs can also help the condition. A diet rich in zinc and essential fatty acids is beneficial, as is cutting out white wine, dairy products and processed foods.

psoriasis treatment

If you suffer from psoriasis, the skin on your scalp renews itself every 48 hours instead of every 28 days, resulting in a flaky scalp. To treat, try using a mild or moisturising shampoo and work the product into the scalp thoroughly. If the scalp is not meticulously clean it creates a perfect breeding ground for bacteria. Shampooing will lift off dead skin cells, but if the shampoo application is too rapid the dead skin cells will flake off when the scalp and hair have dried. Make sure you rinse the hair thoroughly after shampooing, as insufficient rinsing may lead to further scalp irritation. Psoriasis can either be helped or exacerbated by eating certain foods. Oily fish such as trout and salmon contain omega-3 fatty acids and vitamin D and have been found to relieve the symptoms, while alcohol, offal, dairy products, animal fats, meat and spices can aggravate the condition. Cut out or cut down on those foods which affect you adversely.

maintenance work

A DOLLOP of shampoo will be sufficient to wash most hair lengths. Don't be fooled into believing that the more shampoo you use the cleaner your hair will be. Simply leave shampoo on for 60 seconds to ensure that it dissolves stubborn dirt and grease.

DON'T THINK that the lathering capability of a shampoo equates with its cleansing ability. Shampoos are often loaded with cheap lathering agents that strip the hair of its natural oils. Use good-quality shampoos only.

SPEND TIME rinsing conditioner from the hair. If you don't rinse the hair thoroughly it can look lank, become greasy soon after washing and can lead to scalp problems.

AFTER CONDITIONING, gently pat the hair dry. Excessive rubbing with a towel will dishevel the cuticles and weaken the hair.

SPEED UP the conditioning properties of a hair mask by applying the product to freshly washed, towel-dried hair. Wrap cling film around the hair and apply a hot towel. The heat will improve the conditioning benefits. Leave the mask on for 20 minutes, then rinse.

ALWAYS BLOT the hair with a towel to remove excess water before applying conditioner. Only apply conditioner to the lengths and ends of the hair. The scalp should receive sufficient hydration from its oil-producing glands.

IF HAIR smells of smoke or unpleasant cooking aromas and you do not have time to wash it, spray a fine mist of perfume onto your brush and run it through your hair.

NEVER BRUSH wet hair—it is susceptible to damage and prone to breakage. Instead, use a wide-toothed comb and gently work through the hair.

dryers

brushes

combs

hair upkeep

curlers

grips

clips

the right cut

Banish bad hair days by having your hair cut in a style that works in harmony with your hair type. Reputable hairdressers can be found by word of mouth. Listen to your hairdresser's advice, but don't be talked into a style you will not be happy with. It is important to choose a hairstyle that suits your face shape. If you have a round face, choose soft cuts, feathered styles, a lightweight fringe or graduated bobs to help elongate and slim the face. Avoid heavy fringes and curly styles. If you have a square-shaped face, try soft, wavy styles to take the edge off the angular lines of the jaw. Steer clear of geometric cuts, centre partings, heavy fringes and severely scraped-back styles. If you have a long face you can balance the proportions by having a fringe incorporated into your hairstyle. Alternatively, a style that adds width at the jaw can work well. Styles that incorporate texture and body at the sides are good, but avoid sleek haircuts that lie close to the sides of the head, as they will emphasis the length of the face. For a heart-shaped face, opt for styles that are fuller around the jawline, or go for curls at the mid-lengths and ends. Oval faces are considered the perfect shape and can usually carry off any style.

brush basics

brushstrokes

Flat brushes, which are usually oval or rectangular in shape, are ideal for basic work to smooth and detangle the hair. Paddle brushes have large, flat bases, making them suitable for longer lengths. Vent brushes have hollow centres and holes around the bristle base to allow a heated air-stream to flow through the brush while blow-drying, thus speeding up drying time and creating volume. Round or cylindrical brushes are ideal for straightening curly hair, curling straight hair, smoothing sleeker styles or styling short hair. For curling, the smaller the cylinder the tighter the curl. For straightening, smaller brushes—say, 5–8 cm (2–3 inches) in diameter—are suitable for shorter styles, while brushes with a larger diameter should be used on longer hair. To speed up the drying process, choose round brushes which have their bristles embedded in a metal (usually aluminium) barrel. This barrel will heat up when used with a hair-dryer, helping to set and style the hair.

bristle choice

Brushes with natural bristles are less damaging to the hair than synthetic ones, but all-natural bristles can be too soft to penetrate wet or thick hair, which needs the added strength of a mix of nylon and natural bristles. For thick, curly hair, a brush with closely-spaced all-nylon bristles offers maximum control for smoothing or straightening, whereas widely-spaced bristles minimise pull to enhance wave and volume. For fine or thinning hair, use a soft bristle brush. For Afro hair that has been chemically relaxed, use a natural bristle brush. For curly styles, use a wide-toothed comb.

wig work

If you want to undergo a dramatic transformation but have your reservations about what a new style might look like, try on a wig in your desired style, then make your decision. It's also a good way to experiment with new hair colours to find out what does and doesn't suit you.

tools of the trade

hair-dryers

Look for a 1500-watt hair-dryer with at least two speeds and three settings: cool, medium and hot. If you have curly or permed hair, use a diffuser—a plastic or cloth attachment that fits on the end of the dryer's nozzle to gently spread the airflow over your hair without disturbing the curl.

heated rollers

You can set and style your hair within ten minutes with heated rollers. Never use on wet hair, and always spritz the hair with a heat-styling preparation before using. Remove the rollers only when the hair is completely cool, otherwise the curls will drop.

hot brushes

A hot brush can create curls, tame unruly fringes, or flip the ends of the hair up or under. Wind dry (not wet) hair around the brush, working from the ends up, and leave for a few seconds before unwinding.

hair tongs

Choose tongs according to the type of curl you require, remembering that the diameter of the tongs will dictate the size of the curl. If you want to create movement up to the roots, place a comb next to the scalp to form a heat barrier before you wind the tongs down the hair shaft to the roots.

crimping devices

Crimpers are used to create ripples or waves in the hair. They often come with interchangeable attachments to achieve different finishes. Only use crimpers on dry hair, and avoid using on bleached hair, as the high heat created dries the hair and can result in breakages.

straightening irons

These use high heat to flatten the hair, so always use a protective styling spray to reduce the drying effect. Never use on wet or damp hair, and limit your usage of straightening irons to reduce the amount of damage done.

styling products

hair mousse

Mousse gives body to most styles and creates hold without stickiness. It is ideally suited to adding shape and natural body to curly or wavy hair, and thickness and volume to straight hair. Use while drying or styling, but do not apply to wet hair and then leave the hair to dry naturally or it will look stiff and unnatural. If you want more hold, don't apply more product; buy a formulation with extra-holding properties instead.

hair gel

Gel is ideal for moulding and shaping both wet and dry hair. It suits most hair types and styles but should be avoided on very fine hair, as it can weigh the hair down. Never be heavy-handed with application. To prevent lumpy build-up in the hair, massage the gel between your fingertips before applying. If your style has dropped and the hair needs re-styling, do not add more gel. Simply dampen your hands and run them through the hair.

volume enhancers

Heat-activated liquid resins double the width of the hair shaft to add body to a style. These volume enhancers are ideal for limp, fine hair, or for medium-textured hair that lacks body. Apply to damp or dry hair before heat styling.

curl activators

Designed to add definition and shape to naturally curly or permed hair, these preparations are usually a combined gel/conditioner that nourish as they enhance. Don't attempt to use a curl activator on straight hair, as the product will only work on curls.

straightening balms

These are ideal to use on wavy or curly hair that is temporarily being straightened. Although Afro hair usually requires chemical relaxing to straighten, these preparations can be used as a styling aid. They are good for reducing frizz and for protecting the hair against the damage caused by heat styling.

finishing preparations

hairspray

Hairspray is great for holding hair in place and for reducing static. Find a hairspray that works in harmony with your hair type and offers the holding properties you require. Aim to keep the finish natural-looking. This is best done by applying the spray sparingly.

hair wax

Wax works wonders on medium or thick hair, Afro hair and shorter styles that require texture. Apply sparingly, and avoid if you have fine hair. Wax can be hard to wash out of the hair and a build up can make the hair look dull and lifeless. Either apply shampoo to dry hair and then wash as normal, or use a water-soluble wax.

shine enhancers

These are serums, sprays or creams that coat the hair with a film of shine-enhancing silicone. Use as a temporary seal for split ends, to tame stray hairs, revive dull hair and prevent hair going frizzy. Use a shine-enhancer as a post-styling preparation.

hair pomade

Similar to wax, pomade will repel water and atmospheric moisture to help prevent the hair going frizzy. It is ideal for taming Afro and thick hair, and is useful as a finishing preparation on straight hair or as an enhancer for curls. Avoid formulations that are too heavy, as they can be hard to shift and give a very unnatural finish.

product performance

HAIR CONDITIONER makes a good moisturiser for the dry skin on your elbows and knees if you discover you've run out of regular moisturiser.

IF YOU run out of styling product to slick your hair back, use a rich, oil-based moisturiser instead.

TO ENSURE smooth, hair-free legs, use hair conditioner while shaving. It gives a clean shave and has the advantage of containing hydrating extracts which condition the skin.

HAIR SERUM can be used to protect and polish the tresses but can also be smoothed onto bare legs to give the skin a flattering finish in the summer.

HAIR WAX can be used to temporarily seal split ends and style the hair. It can also be massaged into dry cuticles on your nails to help hydrate and protect.

SNAGGED TIGHTS can be prevented from turning into unsightly ladders by spraying the area with hairspray.

MAKE-UP ARTISTS recommend using hair gel to tame unruly eyebrows. Once you've styled your hair, simply run any excess gel through the brows using your fingertips or a comb.

JOJOBA OIL makes a good substitute for styling preparation for those with very dry or Afro hair. Comb the oil through your hair and style as usual.

texture

volume

definition

styling tips

shape

body

finish

dry techniques

blow-drying

Hair is healthiest if dried naturally, but sometimes we need a bit of extra help to hurry things along. For the best blow-drying results, rough-dry your hair with the dryer on a medium heat until it is 50%–60% dry if curly, and 80% dry if straight. Then style and finish drying on a high heat. Move the dryer around constantly as you work over the hair. Direct the airflow down the hair shaft to ensure that the cuticles lie flat (and thus make hair look shiny). To make this task easier, hold the dryer around the base of the nozzle, not the handle. When each section of hair is dry, blast it with cool air to set it, and then move on to the next section.

texture twist

To create an interesting texture, plait hair when it is wet. Leave to dry and then unravel. Run your fingers through the hair to break up the texture. You might also like to experiment with sculpting lotions and sprays on damp hair. They can create great texture when the hair is dry.

body building

When blow-drying, use a heat-activated volumising product to create instant body. Flip your head upside down and run a vent brush through it while blow-drying. To give hair natural movement, wrap damp hair up in a towel and leave it to dry inside the towel.

styling tips

straighten up

The secret to achieving really straight hair lies in the amount of heat you use. Dampen your hair and then, using a hair-dryer of at least 1500 watts, work from the roots to the ends, brushing hair smooth with a round or paddle brush. Start with the underneath sections of the hair and work from the nape of the neck to the front of the head. Ensure that each section of hair is thoroughly dry before moving on to the next, and finish each section with a blast of cool air to set the hair. Alternatively, blow-dry your hair so it is fairly straight, spritz with hairspray and then run a pair of straightening irons down the lengths of the hair.

root lift

To create root lift, try blow-drying the roots in the opposite direction to the way they normally sit. When hair is nearly dry, style in the usual way the hair falls. To achieve lift around your parting, take several small sections of damp hair and prop up each section with a pin. Leave to dry naturally, and when hair is completely dry remove the pins and work the fingers through the hair. If you want to achieve body and height on the crown area, spritz the hair with styling spray and then apply three large, heated rollers to the hair. Leave in for as long as possible. Remove and gently work the fingers through the hair.

styling tips

curl craze

If your hair is naturally curly, apply equal parts of gel and serum to freshly washed and towel-dried hair and scrunch it into the curls. Leave to dry naturally. This mixture will help with curl definition and prevent frizz. If your hair isn't naturally curly but you want to create waves, take random 5 cm (2 inch) sections of damp hair, twist and scrunch each section into a ball, then secure close to the head with a pin. Leave to dry before unravelling. Do not comb curls; instead, gently work through the hair with your fingers. If you want to use rollers, remember that the size of the roller will dictate the type of curl. (For example, a small roller will make a tight curl.) If you want to curl your hair at high speed, run a bath and keep the bathroom door closed. Put rollers in the hair and get into the bath. The steam in the bathroom will help set the curls. Do not remove rollers until the hair is completely dry.

top knot

You don't need to be a pro to get to grips with putting your hair up. One of the easiest styles is to first secure the hair in a ponytail (don't use hair-tearing rubber bands; invest in fabric-coated bands instead). Secure the ponytail at the nape of the neck, higher up towards the crown, or somewhere in between. This will form the base of the bun. Then curl the lengths of the ponytail around the base to create a bun. Secure in place with pins. For an interesting finish, splay the ends out. Alternatively, create a roll by twisting the hair up on itself and then splaying the hair out to disguise the ponytail base. Secure with pins. Experiment with hair texture before creating the ponytail: a messier texture will look more contemporary and is easier to create. Try pulling small strands from the bun and have them fall around the face. Accessorise the look with fresh flowers, simple pieces of jewellery or hair slides.

styling fixes

UNWASHED HAIR is easier to handle than washed hair if you want to wear your hair up. The natural oils in the hair make it more pliable and help it stay put.

AN INSTANT body-building boost can be gained by tipping your head upside down and running a brush through your hair. This traps air amongst the hair to create volume.

DO YOU ever wake up and find that your hair won't behave? No time to wash it? A simple solution is to spritz the outer upper layers with a fine mist of water and then blow-dry into place. Alternatively, skip the water spray and simply apply heat from the dryer to re-style at high speed.

GEL USERS take note. If your hair style has begun to lose its shape, simply dampen your fingers and work them through your hair to reactivate the gel.

IF YOU suffer from greasy hair, use the lowest settings on heat-styling appliances. Hot air can activate the scalp's oil-producing glands, leading to excessive greasiness.

TALCUM POWDER takes the clean edge off newly washed hair (blondes only) to make it easier to put up into a bun. Simply massage the talcum powder into your scalp. If your hair is a darker shade, use hairspray. Just turn your head upside down and spray some light hairspray into the roots.

boost

treat

care

hair solutions

repair

restore

revive

restoring wisdom

hair food

Research has shown that fat-free diets can leave the hair looking dull and lifeless and can increase the possibility of developing a dry scalp. If you notice your hair becoming drier, increase your intake of essential fatty acids. These can be found in vegetable oils, nuts and oily fish. To maintain healthy hair, eat eggs and dairy products, dark-green leafy vegetables, carrots, sweet potatoes and foods rich in zinc, such as wholemeal bread, shellfish and red meat. Note that skipping meals can adversely affect hair condition. Studies have shown that leaving more than 4 hours between meals can starve the hair follicles of essential nutrients, leading to a weakening of the hair.

static charge

All strands of hair have an electric charge, which is either positive or negative. When either two negative or two positive hair strands repel each other, it makes hair go static. This can occur from friction caused when brushing or blow-drying, or when you pull an item of clothing over your head. To instantly tame the charge, spray a comb with hairspray and gently run it through the hair. You can also spray a fine mist of hairspray on a tissue and glide it over the hair. Alternatively, leave-in conditioners, mousse and styling sprays will maintain the balance of the hair and keep it static-free. Use a brush with natural bristles, as nylon bristles aggravate static problems.

colour solutions

orderly advice

A cut and colour go hand in hand, but have the colour done first and then have it cut. Cutting the hair after colouring removes the damaged ends and makes the hair more resilient and appear healthier.

colour correction

Chlorine is very damaging to the hair. It strips moisture from it and can turn bleached or blonde hair an unsightly shade of green (the chemicals in the water oxidise hair colour). To prevent damage and discoloration, use hair products designed to protect the hair from chlorinated water, and always wash your hair with a clarifying shampoo straight after swimming. If your hair does have a green tinge, follow this correcting method: pour tomato juice into the hair, massage in, leave for a couple of minutes and rinse out. The juice will neutralise the green colour and help restore blondes to their former glory.

right timing

After the hair has been coloured, do not wash it or expose it to chlorinated water for 48 hours. If you have had a perm, wait at least 48 hours before using a colorant. Aim to colour your hair 4–6 weeks before going on a holiday in the sun so that it has time to settle before being exposed to harmful UV rays. Protect coloured hair from the sun's rays by wearing a hat to guard against colour fade, dryness and damage, or shield hair with preparations enriched with UV protectors.

hot hair

Even though modern colorants are kind to the hair, hair still requires gentle handling after chemical processing. Don't use too many heat-styling appliances, but if you do use tools such as heated tongs, rollers or straightening irons, always apply a heat-resistant styling preparation to the hair in order to protect it. If you use a hair-dryer, work with it on a cool setting.

mane attraction

fringe benefits

If you want to trim your fringe, take a tip from the experts: comb your fringe into a ponytail so the hair falls in the centre of the forehead between the eyes and then secure with a rubber band. Then, using a pair of sharp scissors, chip into the ends for a natural-looking effect. Always leave the hair slightly longer than required, as it will spring up naturally.

handy help

If your shampoo and conditioner come in glass bottles, place a rubber band around the bottles to prevent them slipping through soapy hands. If you don't like the look of the containers your hair products come in, decant them into stylish pump dispensers.

salt solution

To decrease the amount of damaging residue left by salt water in your hair, apply hair wax before you go for a swim in the ocean. Shampoo out of your hair when you leave the beach.

coming clean

Wash hairbrushes and combs regularly in hot, soapy water. To remove the residue from styling preparations that can build up on tongs, crimpers and straightening irons, use a small amount of surgical spirit and wipe clean with a damp cloth. Ensure you clean the filter of your hair-dryer periodically; a blocked filter will cause the dryer to overheat.

split ends

The only way to banish split ends is to cut them. If you leave split ends, the hair will become more susceptible to damage. Aim to have your hair trimmed every six weeks to prevent split ends. As a short-term measure, seal them by slicking with Vaseline or hair wax.

combination hair

Hair that is oily at the roots and dry at the ends doesn't require numerous products. Choose a shampoo for oily hair and apply conditioner only to the mid-lengths and ends of the hair.

hair snippets

make amends

Afro hair often has fine strands around the hairline resulting from breakages. Use a small, round hairbrush and a hair-dryer to blend with the rest of the hair. To blow-dry chemically relaxed hair, use a heat-styling product and get to work with a vent brush.

wrong formula

If your hair feels rough and dry after shampooing, it could be an indication of the fact that the shampoo you are using is too harsh for your hair.

scalp care

Don't apply hairspray any closer than 5 cm (2 inches) from the roots, unless the product is designed specifically for the roots. Close application can clog the follicles on the scalp.

pillow talk

If you wake up every morning to find your hair dishevelled, try changing your pillowcase. Cotton often causes friction where the hair rubs against it, whereas a satin pillowcase allows the hair to slide over the fabric. Satin will also be kinder on the complexion.

styling preparations

Styling preparations can leave your hair looking dull and lifeless if you overuse them, so make sure you're not too heavy-handed with your application.

colour changes

When melanin production stops, the hair that grows is white, not grey, as commonly perceived. Tints, highlights, lowlights and temporary colorants can be used to bring the colour back.

shine solutions

deep clean

Pollution, city grime, styling preparations, sweat, chlorine and salt water can all leave a residue on the hair, making it look dull and lifeless. Treat the hair once a fortnight with a detoxing shampoo. This type of shampoo contains higher concentrations of cleansers than normal shampoos, and increased levels of chelators ('chela' is Latin for claw), which bind to the surface of the hair to remove collected minerals.

shine enhancers

Dull hair can result from bad circulation, a sluggish metabolism, a build-up of styling preparations, the use of harsh shampoos or a poor diet. To make hair more lustrous, step up your intake of pantothenic acid, an oily acid found in wheatgerm, rice and peanuts. After shampooing the hair, rinse with the juice of a lemon or a capful of vinegar diluted in 1 litre (4 cups) of cold water. This solution will ensure the cuticles lie flat to promote shiny-looking locks.

finishing rinses

Use cold water as a final rinse after conditioning. This closes and flattens the cuticles to ensure optimal shine. If hair is limp, mix 1 cup of flat beer with 3 cups of water. Pour over the hair, massage in for 60 seconds, then rinse out. A herbal rinse for blondes can be made by steeping five chamomile tea bags in boiling water until the water cools. Brunettes can try a rinse of cold coffee or liquorice tea.

scalp rebalancer

Often confused with dandruff, a flaky scalp is actually just the superficial skin cells of the scalp coming off. Use a mild shampoo and wash the hair frequently. Rebalance the scalp after shampooing by massaging it with a mixture of equal quantities of mouthwash and witch-hazel. Leave on overnight and then rinse out. More niacin—a vitamin B6 complex—in your diet can also improve a scaly scalp. Eat more red meat, bread and fortified breakfast cereals.

Index

This edition published in 2000 by
Merehurst Limited, Ferry House,
51–57 Lacy Road, Putney, London SW15 1PR.

Published by Murdoch Books®,
GPO Box 1203, Sydney, NSW Australia 1045.

Photographer: Chris Craymer
Creative Director/Stylist: Jane Campsie
Concept & Design: Marylouise Brammer
Project Manager: Anna Waddington
Editor: Susan Gray
Hair Stylist: Martyn Gale
Make-up Artist: Attracta Courtney
Shoot Production: Susie Bluett at Susie Bluett Productions
Models: Kate Elson, Lottie Greenwood, Molly Hallam, Sarah Hannon, Irmina, Max, Mebrak, Nat, Jennifer McKechnie, Kate Orr, Marie-Claire Rogerso, Sarah-Anne Strandring, Gloria Wong

CEO & Publisher: Anne Wilson
Associate Publisher: Catie Ziller
General Manager: Mark Smith
Production Manager: Liz Fitzgerald
International Sales Director: Kevin Lagden
Marketing & Sales Manager: Kathryn Harvey

A catalogue record for this book is available from the British Library. ISBN 1 85391 931 4.

Distributed in the UK by Macmillan, Houndmills, Basingstoke, Hampshire RG21 6XS.
Telephone (0) 1256 329242

Printed by Toppan Printing Hong Kong Co. Ltd.
PRINTED IN CHINA. First printed 2000.